C
JAC

ADAPTED BY
CIARAN MURTAGH

ILLUSTRATED BY
WILL MORRIS

THE
CALL
OF THE
WILD

Contents

OXFORD
UNIVERSITY PRESS

Chapter 1: Stolen

Buck lived in an impressive house in the Santa Clara valley, California. The house stood back from the road and had a wide, cool veranda that ran round its four sides.

Although Buck belonged to Judge Miller, he was not a kennel dog: he was considered part of the family.

Buck!

Good dog!

Everybody loved Buck.

He would go hunting and swimming with the judge's sons.

Hey! Stop splashing, Buck!

Ha, ha, ha!

He would escort the judge's daughters on twilight or early morning walks.

Fetch!

CHOMP!

And on long wintry nights, he lay at the judge's feet before a roaring fire.

Ahhhhh!

Life was good for Buck.

But all that was about to change ...

Manuel, the judge's gardener, was heavily in debt.

This way, Buck ...

Buck trusted Manuel, so he followed him out through the orchard at the back of the house to the woods beyond.

Just a little further.

I've kept my side of the bargain ...

Buck heard the chink of money.

What's going on?

This'll control 'im plenty.

You're my dog now!

Never had Buck been so vilely treated, and never in all his life had he been so angry.

Wait until I get my teeth into you!

SNARL!

Later ...

Whoooowhooo!

Grrrrrrrr!

For two days and nights, Buck travelled in the crate; for two days and nights, Buck neither ate nor drank.

Finally, the crate was unloaded and taken to a yard.

He's your problem now ...

Who's your master?

SNAP!

Who's your master?

wHACK!

Better.

Whimper Whine

Buck was beaten but not broken. He had learned the lesson of the club, and he never forgot it.

However, Buck's travels were far from over.

Buck was sold again: this time to two men called Francois and Perrault.

He's all yours.

He's one in a thousand that dog ... One in ten thousand!

Buck met his travel companions ...

Calm yourself, Spitz!

Grrrrrrr!

Some were more approachable than others.

Day and night the ship throbbed to the tireless pulse of the propeller. The weather grew steadily colder.

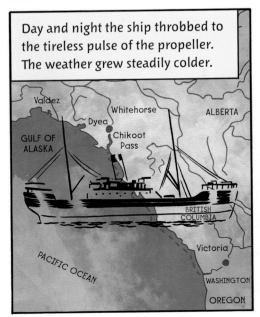

Valdez
Whitehorse
Dyea
ALBERTA
Chikoot Pass
GULF OF ALASKA
BRITISH COLUMBIA
Victoria
PACIFIC OCEAN
WASHINGTON
OREGON

At last, one morning the propeller went quiet.

Chapter 2: The land of snow

Buck had to learn other new skills too ...

He found out why he had been brought to this icy place. He was there to pull sleds.

Francois was stern, demanding obedience, but Buck did his best even though it was new and strange to him.

It was time for the real work to begin. Their job was to take government dispatches and other mail to the town of Dawson.

Keep up!

At first Buck found the work hard.

Mush, lads! Mush!

But as they travelled, day after day, Buck felt his muscles grow strong.

Buck proved his worth time and again; he became an invaluable member of the team.

He was born to be on the ice.

The strongest dog I've ever seen.

HOWL!

Chapter 3: Showdown

Dawson, Yukon, Canada.

Here we are!

Rest up, boys!

Buck soon became a dog that demanded respect. A dog that others feared.

SNARL!

SNARL!

The more accepted Buck became the more Spitz loathed him.

HOWL!

You'll never be as good as me.

SNARL!

I'll be *better* than you.

Grrr!

After a week's rest and recuperation, the dogs were back in the harness once more.

Buck wanted to do things his way.

Come on! Hurry! Faster!

Grrrrrrr!

You need to know your place.

My place is at the front of the team!

Then you'd better come and take it.

Buck knew the time had come.

Grrrrrr!

SNARL!

When the fight was over, Spitz was dead.

With Spitz gone, Buck took his rightful place.

Buck was an inspirational leader ...

Mush! Mush!

Faster, boys! You can do it!

... and soon the team was racing faster than ever.

Dyea Beach ...

Go, Buck!

Woo-hoo!

Yeah!

By the time they got back to base, they were record-breakers.

You're the fastest dog in town!

We're gonna miss you, Buck!

Huh?

Buck and the team were sold to another mailman. They were to haul the post to and from Dawson ... a journey of nearly 1000 miles.

Come on, we've got work to do.

Francois and Perrault were gone from Buck's life.

Buck's new owner worked the team hard, mile after mile across the vast ice.

Mush! Faster!

But the owner was fair.

Come on, boys! We've got a schedule to keep!

A delivery for you, sir!

And so it went on ...

... day ...

... after day ...

... after day.

Until finally they were back in Dyea.

I could sleep for days ...

Even though the mailman could see the dogs were tired and needed rest, he had to sell them on.

Chapter 4: Toil and trouble

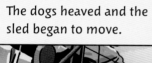

Soon the food ran out.

Come on! Wake up!

There was nothing Buck could do.

This is all your fault!

We've no time for this!

As dogs began to die, those remaining were obliged to pull the sled alone.

Buck's strength dwindled daily.

CRACK!

You too!

I can't go any further.

Regardless of the threat of beatings, Buck was physically incapable of moving.

Just leave me here ...

Do as I say!

CRACK!

Hit that dog again and you'll have me to answer to.

He's practically dead anyway. Keep him!

Mush! Mush!

It's OK, boy. They can't hurt you now.

Chapter 5: Life with Thornton

As spring returned Buck lay by the riverbank, listening to the songs of birds and the hum of nature, and slowly got better.

He made new friends ...

... and as his new master grew stronger, so did he.

You saved me.

Even though he was devoted to Thornton, Buck could hear a call sounding from deep in the forest; he felt compelled to seek it out ...

... so Buck began to explore.

What are you?

RIBBIT!

?!

Soon Buck was feeling at one with the nature around him.

When Buck and Thornton were both recovered, it was time to set off again: Thornton and his friends were also on the search for gold.

Later on that day ...

Watch out!

Arrgghhhh!

SPLASH!

Help!

Go get him, boy!

Buck's coming!

SPLASH!

The eastward journey took them many arduous months.

They travelled across beautiful mountain lakes and through lush green valleys.

All the while, Buck never left Thornton's side.

Finally their wandering came to an end: they came to a broad valley where gold sparkled in the rivers.

This is it, boys!

At last!

We're gonna be rich!

Buck spent long hours musing by the fire as he watched the men at work.

Thornton and his friends worked tirelessly for many days heaping their treasure up.

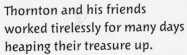

Buck was content, but there was something tugging at him.

Irresistible impulses seized him and made him wander further from camp each day.

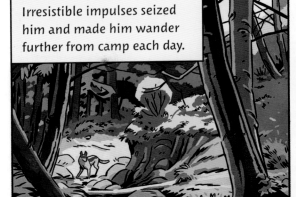

Buck began to feel more at home in the wilderness than with the men who had brought him there.

One night ...

HOWL!

Buck heard a new call. It made his nostrils quiver and his fur bristle.

What was that?

The call was insistent.

HOWL!

I must leave Thornton for now!

HOWL!

Don't be scared.

That tickles!

This way!

The timber wolf started off at an easy lope.

Buck and his new companion played and explored all night and much of the next day.

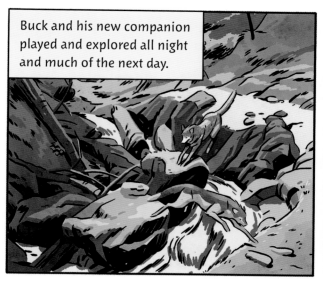

Buck had never felt so alive nor more connected to the world around him.

Until ...

Buck! Buck!

Thornton!

Buuuuuck!

Sorry.

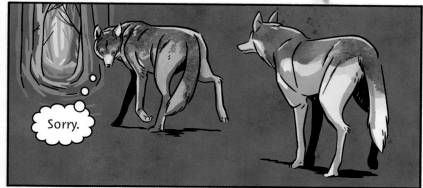

Chapter 6: Running with wolves

For many days Buck mourned Thornton.

Then one day ...

Buck joined the pack, running side by side with his wild brothers.

When the pack leader died, Buck took his place.

Stories were told of the loyal, savage dog who ran with wolves ... Buck became a legend.

But the legendary dog never forgot where he had come from ...

... or who he had become.

Jack London was born in San Francisco in 1876. He spent much of his youth travelling and exploring, and in 1897 he and his sister's husband journeyed to the Klondike in the great Gold Rush. When he wrote *The Call of the Wild*, in 1903, he drew on many of the experiences from his Klondike adventures for material. Jack died in 1916, at the age of forty, having written many novels and stories in his relatively short life.

The Klondike Gold Rush

In 1896 gold was discovered in the Klondike region of Canada. This prompted many men and women, called *prospectors*, to journey to the Klondike to seek their fortune. The Klondike was a cold and remote place, but that didn't stop an estimated 100 000 people, including Jack London, from making the journey in the few short years the rush lasted. In that time, small and remote communities, such as Dawson and Dyea, grew to accommodate the prospectors that travelled to the area. The gold rush ended in 1899 when gold was found elsewhere in Canada and Alaska.